Uke'n Play

UKULELE

MIKE AND DIANE JACKSON

hinkler

About the Authors

Mike and Diane Jackson have spent a large part of their life inspiring, encouraging and empowering music making in people of all ages.

A self-taught musician who plays 16 different instruments, including ukulele, Mike is perhaps best known for his hit version of *Bananas in Pyjamas*. He has sold over 250,000 albums, published many song-and-dance resources and performed extensively across Australia and internationally. Mike' s inspirational concerts and workshops attest to his belief that learning to play music is an attainable goal for everyone and that it' s never, ever too late – or too early – to begin!

Diane has a Graduate Diploma in Music Education and many years' experience teaching classroom music and running community music classes for young children.

Using the *Uke' n Play Ukulele* resources, many who previously thought themselves 'not musical' have fulfilled a lifelong dream of playing an instrument.

hinkler

Published by Hinkler Books Pty Ltd
45–55 Fairchild Street
Heatherton Victoria 3202 Australia
www.hinkler.com.au

© Larrikin Music Publishing Pty Ltd 2013
Layout and design © Hinkler Books Pty Ltd 2013

All songs traditional with arrangement by Mike Jackson, apart from: The Ballad of Eensy Weensy – Traditional. This arrangement by Mike Jackson. Words: chorus traditional, verses Mike Jackson; Oh, Susanna – This arrangement by Mike Jackson. Words and music: Stephen Collins Foster; Five Little Monkeys – Traditional. This arrangement by Mike Jackson. Words verse 6: Mike Jackson and Ian Blake; Ukulele Lady – Words and music by Gus Khan and Richard A. Whiting

Authors: Mike and Diane Jackson
Cover design: Sam Grimmer
Typesetting: MPS Limited
Prepress: Graphic Print Group

Play-along CD created by ToeTapper Records
Lead vocals: Mike Jackson, Thom Jackson
Ukulele: Diane Jackson, Thom Jackson
Harmonies: Hugh McDonald, Thom Jackson, Ian Blake, Michelle Berner
Instrumentalists: Mike Jackson (ukulele, concertina, melodeon, harmonica), Hugh McDonald (bass, strings), Ian Blake (horns, keyboards, whistles, silly voices), Dave Folley (drums)
Recorded at Hugh McDonald Studios, Melbourne, Australia 2005–2010
Recorded, engineered and mixed by Hugh McDonald
Remixed and compiled 2013

ISBN: 978 1 4889 3062 1

Printed and bound in China

Contents

Getting Started

- Become familiar with the parts of your ukulele.
- Gently stretch your ukulele strings.
- Listen to track 1 to become familiar with the ukulele notes.
- Tune the strings carefully.

Tuning the Ukulele

There are several methods you can use to tune your ukulele. The open string names are G, C, E and A. 'Open' means no fingers pressing the strings to the fretboard.

Tuning Track (Track 1)

Play the open strings, starting from the string closest to your head. Turn the tuning peg a little to check which way makes the string higher or lower, then tune the string to the correct note. To remember the notes for tuning the uke, sing 'My Dog Has Fleas'. This classic uke tuning song is sung on the tuning track and uses the notes G, C, E and A.

Piano

G — First G above middle C

C — Middle C

E — First E above middle C

A — First A above middle C

Electronic Tuner

A clip-on tuner is the best option as it is unaffected by noise in the immediate area and takes only the note from the ukulele. Tuners are also available for computers or smartphones. Software and applications for a chromatic tuner or specific ukulele tuner work best in a quiet room.

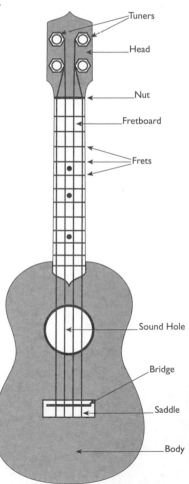

Mike Jackson's Instant Play Method

This system is simple, but it works!

The Ukulele

The coloured dots on your ukulele fretboard help you remember where to place your fingers and will make your chord changes much quicker.

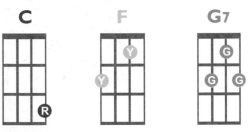

The Song Book

The chord names in the song pages have been coloured to match the dots: **C** = red, F = yellow, **G7** = green.

F   **C**   **G7**
Oh! Susanna, don't you cry for me.

Making Chords

Rest the body of the ukulele in your lap with its neck pointing upwards at about 45° and with the strings away from you (see page 6). Use your right forearm to hold the instrument against your body. Using your left hand, gently place your thumb (facing up) on the dot at the back of the fretboard.

Use the tips of your fingers to gently press the strings onto the correct dots for the chord you are going to play. Make sure you use the correct finger for each dot and that your finger only touches the string that you are pressing down.

Finger numbering:
1 — index finger
2 — middle finger
3 — ring finger

Chord Diagrams

C Chord

Place your ring finger (3) on the red dot.

F Chord

Place your pointer and middle finger (1 and 2) on the yellow dots.

G7 Chord

Place your pointer finger (1) on the green dot nearest the nut and place your middle finger (2) and ring finger (3) on the other green dots.

Ukulele Chords Used in this Book

C	C7	Cmaj7	C6	Dm	D7

Em7	F	F7	G7	A♭7	Am

Strumming

Like a drummer, the ukulele player must keep the beat, so keep your strumming constant through the whole song. Begin by using either 'down' or 'down-up-down-up' strums and play with the back/s of your fingernail/s, the side of your thumb, or a felt or soft rubber pick, which can be purchased from music stores.

Strumming Styles (Track 52)

1	VVVV	'down' strums
2	V∧V∧	'down/up' strums
3	4 V 4 V	pick the 'G' or 4th string with the back of your index finger (the nail) then play a 'down' strum with your fingernail/s

Chord Patterns (Track 53)

Once you can play the C, F and G7 chords, try repeating these chord patterns with 4 strums on each chord. If a particular chord change is giving you trouble, slow down (or play 8 strums on each chord) and practise only that change until you are comfortable with it.

1 F   C   F   C
   VVVV VVVV VVVV VVVV

2 C   G7   C   G7
   VVVV VVVV VVVV VVVV

3 C   F   G7   C
   VVVV VVVV VVVV VVVV

4 C   F   C   G7
   VVVV VVVV VVVV VVVV

Hints

- Be patient! Give your hands plenty of time to learn new tricks and above all, relax when you're learning them. The more tense you are, the harder it is to learn and the more likely you are to make your hands sore.
- The skin on your fingertips will gradually become harder, so play for short periods when you first begin.
- Strings only have to touch the fret to change a note, so you don't need to press hard.
- You can practise chord changes silently while watching TV! Just do the chord changes without strumming.

1. Row, Row, Row Your Boat

C

C
Row, row, row your boat, gently down the stream

Merrily, merrily, merrily, merrily

Life is but a dream

(× 3)

Place your ring finger (3) on red dot

C
Row, row, row your boat, gently down the stream

Putt putt, splutter splutter

Out of gasoline!

C
Row, row, row your boat, underneath the stream

Ha! Ha! fooled you

I'm a submarine!

C
Row, row, row your boat, gently down the stream

If you see a crocodile

Don't forget to scream (Aaahhh!)

2. Christmas Is Coming

C

C

Christmas is coming and the geese are getting fat

Please put a penny in the old man's hat

If you haven't got a penny, a ha'penny will do

If you haven't got a ha'penny well Lord bless you!

Ring finger (3) on red dot

REPEAT × 1

INSTRUMENTAL

REPEAT × 1

3. Three Blind Mice

C

C
Three blind mice, three blind mice
C
See how they run, see how they run
C
They all ran after the farmer's wife
C
Who cut off their tails with a carving knife
C
Did ever you see such a thing in your life
C
As three blind mice?

REPEAT

4. Frère Jacques/R2D2/Young Bart Simpson

F

F

Frère Jacques, Frère Jacques,

Dormez-vous, dormez-vous?

Sonnez les matines, sonnez les matines

Din, din, don! Din, din, don!

F

Are you sleeping, are you sleeping,

Brother John, Brother John?

Morning bells are ringing, morning bells are ringing

Ding, dang, dong! Ding, dang, dong!

F

R2D2, R2D2

C3PO, C3PO

Obi Wan Kenobi, Obi Wan Kenobi

Han Solo, Han Solo.

F

Young Bart Simpson, young Bart Simpson

Lisa too, Lisa too

Marge and baby Maggie, Marge and baby Maggie

Homer too, Homer too.

Pointer (1) and middle (2) fingers on yellow dots

5. Polly Wolly Doodle

F   **C**

Oh, I went down south for to see my gal, sing Polly Wolly Doodle all the day

                                     F

My Sal she is a saucy gal, sing Polly Wolly Doodle all the day

CHORUS:

F   **C**

Fare thee well, fare thee well, fare thee well, my fairy fay

> Pointer (1) and middle (2) fingers on yellow dots for F, then change to ring finger (3) on red dot for C

For I'm goin' to Louisiana, for to see my Susyanna

                        F

Sing Polly Wolly Doodle all the day

                                     C

Fare thee well, fare thee well, fare thee well, my fairy fay

For I'm goin' to Louisiana, for to see my Susyanna

                        F

Sing Polly Wolly Doodle all the day

F   **C**

Grasshopper sitting on a railroad track, sing Polly Wolly Doodle all the day

                                        F

He was picking his teeth with a carpet tack, sing Polly Wolly Doodle all the day

CHORUS

6. It Ain't Gonna Rain No More

CHORUS:

F
It ain't gonna rain no more, no more

              C
It ain't gonna rain no more

How in the heck can I wash my neck

                  F
When the wash rag's on the floor

F
We had a cat down on our farm

        C
It ate a ball of yarn

When those little kittens were born

           F
They all had sweaters on

CHORUS

F
We had a goat down on our farm

        C
It ate up old tin cans

And when those little goats were born

           F
They came in Ford sedans

CHORUS × 2

7. Miss Mary Mac

C   F

F
Miss Mary Mac, Mac, Mac

All dressed in black, black, black

With silver buttons, buttons, buttons
          C
All down her back, back, back

She asked her mother, mother, mother

For 50 cents, cents, cents

To see the elephants, elephants, elephants
        F
Jump over the fence, fence, fence

          F
They jumped so high, high, high

They reached the sky, sky, sky

And they didn't came back, back, back
          C
Till the 4th of July, ly, ly

Miss Mary Mac, Mac, Mac

All dressed in black, black, black

With silver buttons, buttons, buttons
        F
All down her back, back, back

8. The Ballad of Eensy Weensy

CHORUS:
```
C                         F           C
Eensy Weensy Spider climbed up the waterspout
                    F              C
Down came the rain and washed poor Eensy out
F          C         F
Out came the sunshine and dried up all the rain
       C                     F          C
So the Eensy Weensy Spider climbed up the spout again
```

```
C                         F          C
The spider climbed the spout and she gave a little cheer
                    F           C
I'm almost at the top and my journey's end is near
      F          C        F
Then she heard a clap of thunder and down came lots of rain
       C                 F          C
And both she and all her hopes went sadly down the drain
```

```
C                         F          C
As she lay there at the bottom the poor spider felt quite done
                    F          C
But, as very often happens, after rain there came the sun
F              C      F
The Eensy Weensy Spider soon was warm and dry
       C                 F          C
So she headed for the spout again to have another try
```

CHORUS

```
C                     F          C
The moral of this story is one I'm sure you know
                    F          C
If you don't make it the first time then have another go
F          C         F
And take a little lesson from the spider in this song
       C                 F          C
Then if you're at the bottom, you won't stay there for long
```

9. Oh, Dear! What Can the Matter Be?

CHORUS:
F
Oh, dear! What can the matter be?
C
Dear, dear! What can the matter be?
F
Oh, dear! What can the matter be?
C   **F**
Johnny's so long at the fair

F
He promised to buy me a trinket to please me
    C
And then for a smile, oh, he vowed he would tease me
    F
He promised to buy me a bunch of blue ribbons
    C   **F**
To tie up my bonnie brown hair

    CHORUS

F
He promised to bring me a basket of posies
    C
A garland of lilies, a gift of red roses
    F
A little straw hat to set off the blue ribbons
    C   **F**
That tie up my bonnie brown hair

    CHORUS

10. Mary Had a Little Lamb

F   C   F
Mary had a little lamb, little lamb, little lamb
                       C   F
Mary had a little lamb whose feet were black as soot
                 C   F
Everywhere that Mary went, Mary went, Mary went
                 C   F
Everywhere that Mary went it put its sooty foot

F   C   F
Mary had another lamb, 'nother lamb, 'nother lamb
                      C   F
Mary had another lamb whose fleas were white as snow
                       C   F
And everywhere that Mary went, Mary went, Mary went
                 C   F
Everywhere that Mary went the fleas were sure to go

F   C   F
Mary had a little lamb, little lamb, little lamb
                   C   F
Mary had a little lamb its fleece was white as snow

13. The Farmer's in the Dell

F
The farmer's in the dell, the farmer's in the dell
          C   F
Eee-i-addy-o, the farmer's in the dell

The farmer takes a wife, the farmer takes a wife
          C   F
Eee-i-addy-o, the farmer takes a wife

The wife takes a child, the wife takes a child
          C   F
Eee-i-addy-o, the wife takes a child

F
The child takes the dog, the child takes the dog
          C   F
Eee-i-addy-o, the child takes the dog

The dog takes the cat, the dog takes the cat
          C   F
Eee-i-addy-o, the dog takes the cat

The cat takes the mouse, the cat takes the mouse
          C   F
Eee-i-addy-o, the cat takes the mouse

F
The mouse takes the cheese, the mouse takes the cheese
          C   F
Eee-i-addy-o, the mouse takes the cheese

F
The cheese stands alone!!

14. Blow the Man Down

C
Come all you young fellows that follows the sea
G7
To me way, hey, blow the man down!

Now please pay attention and listen to me
             C
Give me some time to blow the man down

    CHORUS:
    C
    Blow the man down bullies, blow the man down
      G7
    To me way, hey, blow the man down!

    Blow her right back home to Liverpool Town
                C
    Oh, give me some time to blow the man down

C
On a trim Black Ball liner, I first served me time
      G7
To me way, hey, blow the man down!

On a trim Black Ball liner, I wasted me prime
             C
Oh, give me some time to blow the man down

    CHORUS

C
When a trim Black Ball liner's preparing for sea
      G7
To me way, hey, blow the man down!

You'd split your sides laughing, such sights you would see
            C
Oh, give me some time to blow the man down

    CHORUS

C
Well, there are tinkers and tailors and cobblers and all
       G7
To me way, hey, blow the man down!

They're all shipped for sailors on board the Black Ball
           C
Oh, give me some time to blow the man down

    CHORUS

A ³/₄ song again – strum in 3s

15. This Old Man

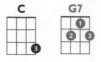

C
This old man, he played one
G7
He played knick-knack on my drum

    CHORUS:
          C
    With a knick-knack, paddy whack, give the dog a bone
    G7   **C**
    This old man came rolling home

C
This old man, he played two
G7
He played knick-knack on my shoe

    CHORUS

C
This old man, he played three
G7
He played knick-knack on my knee

    CHORUS

C
This old man, he played four
G7
He played knick-knack on my door

    CHORUS

C
This old man, he played five
G7
He played knick-knack on my hive

CHORUS

C
This old man, he played six
G7
He played knick-knack on my sticks

CHORUS

C
This old man, he played seven
G7
He played knick-knack up in heaven

CHORUS

C
This old man, he played eight
G7
He played knick-knack on my gate

CHORUS

C
This old man, he played nine
G7
He played knick-knack on my spine

CHORUS

C
This old man, he played ten
G7
He played knick-knack home again

CHORUS

16. London Bridge Is Falling Down

C   F

F
London Bridge is falling down
C   F
Falling down, falling down

London Bridge is falling down
C   F
My fair lady

F
Build it up with sticks and stones
C   F
Sticks and stones, sticks and stones

Build it up with sticks and stones
C   F
My fair lady

F
Sticks and stones will wash away
C   F
Wash away, wash away

Sticks and stones will wash away
C   F
My fair lady

Try strum no. 3 on page 7 for this song

24

F
Build it up with iron and steel
C   F
Iron and steel, iron and steel

Build it up with iron and steel
C   F
My fair lady

F
Iron and steel will bend and bow
C   F
Bend and bow, bend and bow

Iron and steel will bend and bow
C   F
My fair lady

REPEAT VERSE 1

17. Shortnin' Bread

C   G7

CHORUS:
C
Mamma's little babies love shortnin' shortnin'
        G7   **C**
Mamma's little babies love shortnin' bread
C
Mamma's little babies love shortnin' shortnin'
        G7   **C**
Mamma's little babies love shortnin' bread

Play 2 strums only on G7 before changing back to C

C
Three little babies lyin' in bed
        G7   **C**
Two were sick and the other half dead

Call for the doctor, the doctor said
        G7   **C**
Give those babies some shortnin' bread

    CHORUS

C
Put on the frying pan, put on the lid
        G7   **C**
Mamma's gone make a little shortnin' bread

That isn't all she's gonna do
        G7   **C**
She's gonna give her babies a big hug too

    CHORUS

C
Mamma fed her babies on shortnin' bread
        G7   **C**
She gave them a hug and they jumped out of bed

They danced in the kitchen, they danced in the hall
        G7   **C**
Those three little babies were having a ball

    CHORUS

18. Li'l Liza Jane

C   F

F
I've got a gal and you've got none, Li'l Liza Jane
                               C   F
I've got a gal that calls me "Hon'," Li'l Liza Jane

    CHORUS:
    F
    Oh, Eliza, Li'l Liza Jane
             C   F
    Oh, Eliza, Li'l Liza Jane

F
Come, my love, and live with me, Li'l Liza Jane
                          C   F
I will take good care of thee, Li'l Liza Jane

    CHORUS

F
Liza Jane has come to me, Li'l Liza Jane
                        C   F
We're as happy as can be, Li'l Liza Jane

    CHORUS

F
We have a house in Baltimore, Li'l Liza Jane
                           C   F
Lots of children 'round the door, Li'l Liza Jane

    CHORUS × 2

19. Buffalo Girls

C
Buffalo gals, woncha come out tonight
G7   **C**
Come out tonight, come out tonight

Buffalo gals, woncha come out tonight
     G7   **C**
And dance by the light of the moon

     CHORUS:
       C
     Ain't ya, ain't ya, ain't ya, ain't ya coming out tonight
     G7   **C**
     Coming out tonight, coming out tonight

     Ain't ya, ain't ya, ain't ya, ain't ya coming out tonight
         G7   **C**
     To dance by the light of the moon

C
Danced with the dolly with a hole in her stocking
         G7   **C**
And her feet kept a-rocking and her knees kept a-knocking

Well I danced with the dolly with a hole in her stocking
         G7   **C**
And we danced by the light of the moon

     CHORUS

C
Had a little girl with freckles on her face
G7   **C**
Freckles on her face, freckles on her face

Asked her where she got them, said she got them every place
G7   **C**
Ain't ya, ain't ya coming out tonight

     CHORUS

20. He's Got the Whole World in His Hands

CHORUS:
F
He's got the whole world in His hands
     C
He's got the whole wide world in His hands
     F
He's got the whole world in His hands
     C   F
He's got the whole world in His hands

F
He's got you and me brothers, in His hands
   C
He's got you and me brothers, in His hands
   F
He's got you and me brothers, in His hands
   C   F
He's got the whole world in His hands

CHORUS

F
He's got you and me sisters, in His hands
   C
He's got you and me sisters, in His hands
   F
He's got you and me sisters, in His hands
   C   F
He's got the whole world in His hands

CHORUS

4 strums only on the C chord in the last line

21. Michael Finnigan

C
There was an old man called Michael Finnigan
G7
He grew whiskers on his chin again
   C
The wind came out and blew them in again
G7   **C**
Poor old Michael Finnigan, begin again

Try strum no. 3 on page 7 for this song

C
There was an old man called Michael Finnigan
    G7
Who went off fishing with a pin again
C
Caught a fish, but it fell in again
G7   **C**
Poor old Michael Finnigan, begin again

C
There was an old man called Michael Finnigan
G7
He grew fat and he grew thin again
C
Then he died, and had to begin again
G7   **C**
Poor old Michael Finnigan

REPEAT WHOLE SONG

22. I Saw Three Ships

F
I saw three ships come sailing in
        C
On Christmas Day, on Christmas Day
F
I saw three ships come sailing in
       C F
On Christmas Day in the morning

F
Three pretty maids were on those ships
        C
On Christmas Day, on Christmas Day
F
Three pretty maids were on those ships
       C F
On Christmas Day in the morning

F
What could those three pretty maids do?
        C
On Christmas Day, on Christmas Day
F
What could those three pretty maids do?
       C F
On Christmas Day in the morning

F
One could whistle and one could sing
        C
And one could play the violin
F
Such joy there'll be at my wedding
       C F
On Christmas Day in the morning

    REPEAT VERSE 1 × 2

23. Clementine

C
In a cavern, in a canyon
G7
Excavating for a mine
            C
Dwelt a miner – Forty-niner
     G7   **C**
And his daughter Clementine

CHORUS:
C
Oh my darling, oh my darling
                     G7
Oh my darling, Clementine
                      C
Thou art lost and gone forever
     G7   **C**
Dreadful sorry, Clementine

C
Light she was and like a fairy
                  G7
And her shoes were number nine
            C
Herring boxes without topses
     G7   **C**
Sandals were for Clementine

CHORUS

C
Drove she ducklings to the water
                 G7
Every morning just at nine
                      C
Tripped her foot against a splinter
G7   **C**
Fell into the foaming brine

CHORUS

C
Saw her lips above the water
                G7
Blowing bubbles mighty fine
            C
But alas, I was no swimmer
G7   **C**
So I lost my Clementine

CHORUS

24. O Christmas Tree (O Tannenbaum)

F
O Christmas Tree, O Christmas Tree
  C   F
Your leaves are so unchanging

O Christmas Tree, O Christmas Tree
  C   F
Your leaves are so unchanging

                C
Not only green when summer's here

          F
But also when it's cold and drear

O Christmas Tree, O Christmas Tree
  C   F
Your leaves are so unchanging

F
O Christmas Tree, O Christmas Tree
  C   F
How richly God has decked you

O Christmas Tree, O Christmas Tree
  C   F
How richly God has decked you

         C
You bid us true and faithful be

         F
And trust in God unchangingly

O Christmas Tree, O Christmas Tree
  C   F
How richly God has decked you

25. Skip to My Lou, My Darling

C
Fly's in the buttermilk, shoo, fly, shoo
G7
Fly's in the buttermilk, shoo, fly, shoo
C
Fly's in the buttermilk, shoo, fly, shoo
G7   **C**
Skip to my Lou, my darlin'

CHORUS:
C
Lou, Lou, skip to my Lou
G7
Lou, Lou, skip to my Lou
C
Lou, Lou, skip to my Lou
G7   **C**
Skip to my Lou, my darlin'

C
Cat's in the cream jar, ooh, ooh, ooh
G7
Cat's in the cream jar, ooh, ooh, ooh
C
Cat's in the cream jar, ooh, ooh, ooh
G7   **C**
Skip to my Lou, my darlin'

CHORUS × 2

26. Alouette

F   **C**   F   **C**   F
Alouette, gentille Alouette. Alouette je te plumerai
F   **C**   F   **C**   F
Alouette, gentille Alouette. Alouette je te plumerai
F   **C**   F
Je te plumerai la tête. Je te plumerai la tête
C
Et la tête, et la tête. Alouette, Alouette
C
O-o-o-o-oh

F   **C**   F   **C**   F
Alouette, gentille Alouette. Alouette je te plumerai
F   **C**   F   **C**   F
Alouette, gentille Alouette. Alouette je te plumerai
F   **C**   F
Je te plumerai le nez. Je te plumerai le nez
C
Et le nez, et le nez. Alouette, Alouette
C
O-o-o-o-oh

F   **C**   F   **C**   F
Alouette, gentille Alouette. Alouette je te plumerai
F   **C**   F   **C**   F
Alouette, gentille Alouette. Alouette je te plumerai
F   **C**   F
Je te plumerai les yeux. Je te plumerai les yeux
C
Et les yeux, et les yeux. Alouette, Alouette
C
O-o-o-o-oh

F   **C**   F   **C**   F
Alouette, gentille Alouette. Alouette je te plumerai

27. 'Twas the Night Before Christmas

C   G7

G7   **C**
'Twas the night before Christmas and all through the house
   G7   **C**
Not a creature was stirring, not even a mouse
   G7   **C**
All the stockings were hung by the chimney with care
   G7   **C**
In the hope that Saint Nicholas soon would be there

    G7   **C**
He's bringing lots of toys
   G7   **C**
For girls and boys
   G7   **C**
But wait until you see
   G7   **C**
That merry Christmas tree

    G7   **C**
So on Dasher, on Dancer, on Prancer and Vixen
   G7   **C**
On Comet and Cupid and Donner and Blitzen
    G7   **C**
To the top of the roof, to the top of the wall
     G7   **C**
Here they come and they're saying, "Merry Christmas to all!"

28. Hail! Hail! The Gang's All Here

CHORUS:
F
Hail! Hail! The gang's all here
C
What the heck do we care?

What the heck do we care?
F
Hail! Hail! We're full of cheer
C   F
What the heck do we care Bill!

F
A gang of good fellows are we (are we)

Are we (are we) are we (are we)

With never a worry you see (you see)
        C
You see (you see) you see (you see)
                    F   C   F
We'll sing till morn and never yawn, we'll live life merrily
        C
No matter the weather, when we get together
        F   C
We have a jubilee

CHORUS

F
When out for a good time we go, (we go)

We go, (we go) we go, (we go)

There's nothing we do that is slow, (is slow)
  C
Is slow, (is slow) is slow, (is slow)
      F   C   F
Of joy we get our share you bet, the gang will tell you so
  C
No matter the weather, when we get together
  F   C
We sing this song you know

CHORUS

29. Oh, Susanna

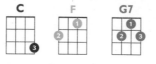

C   G7
I come from Alabama with my banjo on my knee
   C   G7   C
I'm going to Louisiana my true love for to see
                                 G7
It rained all night the day I left, the weather was bone dry
   C   G7   C
The sun so hot I froze to death, Susanna don't you cry

Let's try all 3 chords together now!

  CHORUS:
  F   C   G7
  Oh! Susanna, Don't you cry for me
     C   G7 C
  I come from Alabama, with my banjo on my knee

C   G7
I had a dream the other night, when everything was still
  C   G7   C
I thought I saw Susanna, she was coming down the hill
                              G7
A buckwheat cake was in her mouth, a tear was in her eye
          C   G7   C
Says I, "I'm coming from the south, Susanna don't you cry"

  CHORUS

C   G7
I soon will be in New Orleans and then I'll look around
     C   G7   C
And when I find Susanna, I'll fall upon the ground
                         G7
But if I do not find her, this boy will surely die
     C   G7   C
And when I'm dead and buried, Susanna don't you cry

  CHORUS

30. Angel Band

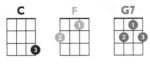

```
C              F    C        G7   C
```
My latest sun is sinking fast, my race is nearly run
```
                F        C            G7   C
```
My strongest trials now are past, my triumph has begun

CHORUS:
```
G7        C
```
Oh, come, Angel Band
```
G7        C
```
Come and around me stand
```
F                    C                      G7   C
```
Bear me away on your snow white wings to my immortal home
```
F                    C                      G7   C
```
Bear me away on your snow white wings to my immortal home

```
C              F   C          G7     C
```
I know I'm near the holy ranks of friends and kindred dear
```
                F        C            G7     C
```
I brush the dew on Jordan's banks, the crossing must be near

CHORUS

```
C                F      C          G7
```
I've almost gained my heavenly home, my spirit loudly sings
```
                F      C            G7   C
```
The holy ones, behold they come – I hear the noise of wings

CHORUS

31. Banks of the Ohio

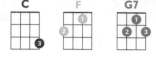

C   G7
I asked my love to take a walk
                    C
To take a walk, just a little way
                              F
And as we walked, then we would talk
C   G7   C
All about our wedding day

CHORUS:
C   G7
Darlin', say that you'll stay with me
                    C
In our home we'll happy be
                        F
Down beside where the waters flow
        C   G7   C
Down by the banks of the Ohio

C   G7
I took her by her pretty white hand
                            C
I led her down the banks of sand
                              F
I plunged her in where she would drown
              C G7   C
And watched her as she floated down

     CHORUS
C   G7
Returnin' home between twelve and one
                        C
Thinkin', Lord, what a deed I've done
                    F
I've killed the girl I love, you see
            C   G7   C
Because she would not marry me

C   G7
The very next day, at half past four
                        C
The sheriff walked right to my door
                          F
He says, "Young man, don't you try to run
        C   G7   C
You'll pay for this awful crime you've done"

     CHORUS

32. Home on the Range

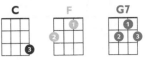

C   **F**
Oh give me a home where the buffalo roam
       C   **G7**
Where the deer and the antelope play
    C   **F**
Where seldom is heard a discouraging word
    C   **G7**   **C**
And the skies are not cloudy all day

     C   **F**
Oh, give me a land where the bright diamond sand
     C   **G7**
Flows leisurely down the stream
       C   **F**
Where the graceful white swan goes gliding along
     C   **G7**   **C**
Like a maid in a heavenly dream

    CHORUS:
    C   **G7**   **C**
    Home, home on the range
                   G7
    Where the deer and the antelope play
        C   **F**
    Where seldom is heard a discouraging word
          C   **G7**   **C**
    And the skies are not cloudy all day

C   **F**
Where the air is so pure, the zephyrs so free
    C   **G7**
The breezes so balmy and light
     C
That I would not exchange my home on the range
    C   **G7**   **C**
For all the cities so bright

    CHORUS

33. Five Little Monkeys

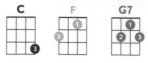

C   G7   C

C   **G7**   **C**
Five little monkeys jumping on the bed
           F   **C**
One fell off and bumped his head
                    F   **C**
Called for the doctor, the doctor said
               G7   **C**
"No more monkeys jumping on the bed!"

C   **G7**   **C**
Four little monkeys jumping on the bed
           F   **C**
One fell off and bumped his head
                    F   **C**
Called for the doctor, the doctor said
               G7   **C**
"No more monkeys jumping on the bed!"

C   **G7**   **C**
Three little monkeys jumping on the bed
           F   **C**
One fell off and bumped his head
                    F   **C**
Called for the doctor, the doctor said
               G7   **C**
"No more monkeys jumping on the bed!"

```
C              G7           C
```
Two little monkeys jumping on the bed
```
              F           C
```
One fell off and bumped his head
```
                       F      C
```
Called for the doctor, the doctor said
```
                  G7           C
```
"No more monkeys jumping on the bed!"

```
C              G7           C
```
One little monkey jumping on the bed
```
              F           C
```
He fell off and bumped his head
```
                       F      C
```
Called for the doctor, the doctor said
```
                  G7              C
```
At least there's no more monkeys on the bed

```
C              G7      C
```
Five little monkeys lying in bed
```
                  F           C
```
Each with a bandage round his head
```
                       F       C
```
Wished they'd listened when the doctor said
```
                  G7           C
```
"No more monkeys jumping on the bed!"

But not for long!

45

34. Frog Went a Courtin'

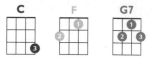

C F G7

C
Frog went a courtin' and he did ride, uh-hum, uh-hum
                                    G7
Frog went a courtin' and he did ride, uh-hum, uh-hum
C   **F**
Frog went a courtin' and he did ride, he rode out to seek a bride
   C   **G7**   **C**
Uh-hum, uh-hum, uh-hum

C
He rode up to Miss Mousie's door, uh-hum, uh-hum
                              G7
He rode up to Miss Mousie's door, uh-hum, uh-hum
C   **F**
He rode up to Miss Mousie's door, vowed he'd love her evermore
   C   **G7**   **C**
Uh-hum, uh-hum, uh-hum

C
"Dear Froggie, yes I'll marry you," uh-hum, uh-hum
                          G7
"Dear Froggie, yes I'll marry you," uh-hum, uh-hum
C   **F**
"Dear Froggie, yes I'll marry you, let's grow old together 'cos I love you too"
     C   **G7**   **C**
Uh-hum, uh-hum, uh-hum

C
First they told her Uncle Rat, uh-hum, uh-hum
                     G7
First they told her Uncle Rat, uh-hum, uh-hum
C   **F**
First they told her Uncle Rat, said "Hey Uncle Rat, what you think about that?"
     C   **G7**   **C**
Uh-hum, uh-hum, uh-hum

C
Next they told two little blank ants, uh-hum, uh-hum
                           G7
Next they told two little blank ants, uh-hum, uh-hum
C   **F**
Next they told two little blank ants, everybody jumped up and they started to dance
   C   **G7**   **C**
Uh-hum, uh-hum, uh-hum

C
What shall the wedding supper be, uh-hum, uh-hum
                         G7
What shall the wedding supper be, uh-hum, uh-hum
C   **F**
What shall the wedding supper be, fried mosquito and a black-eyed pea
   C   **G7**   **C**
Uh-hum, uh-hum, uh-hum

C
Little piece of corn bread layin' on the shelf, uh-hum, uh-hum
                               G7
Little piece of corn bread layin' on the shelf, uh-hum, uh-hum
C   **F**
Little piece of corn bread layin' on the shelf, if you want anymore you can sing it yourself
   C   **G7**   **C**
Uh-hum, uh-hum, uh-hum
   C   **G7**   **C**
Uh-hum, uh-hum, uh-hum
   C   **G7**   **C**
Uh-hum, uh-hum, uh-hum

35. Jingle Bells

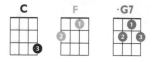

CHORUS:
C
Jingle bells, jingle bells, jingle all the way
F   **C**   **G7**
Oh, what fun it is to ride in a one horse open sleigh – Hey!
C
Jingle bells, jingle bells, jingle all the way
F   **C**   **G7**   **C**
Oh, what fun it is to ride in a one horse open sleigh

C   **F**
Dashing through the snow, in a one horse open sleigh
               G7   **C**
O'er the fields we go, laughing all the way

                             F
Bells on bob tails ring, making spirits bright
               G7   **C**
What fun it is to laugh and sing, a sleighing song tonight

CHORUS 2:
C
Jingle bells, jingle bells, jingle all the way
F   **C**   **G7**
Oh, what fun it is to ride in a one horse open sleigh – Hey!
C
Jingle bells, jingle bells, jingle all the way
F   **C**   **G7**   **C**
Oh, what fun it is to ride in a one horse open sleigh – Hey!

36. Joy to the World

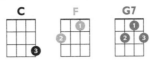

C   G7   C
Joy to the world! The Lord is come
   F   G7   C
Let earth receive her King!
     FC   F   C
Let every heart prepare Him room

And heaven and earth shall sing
 G7
And heaven and earth shall sing
   C   F   G7   C
And heaven and heaven and earth shall sing!

C   G7   C
Joy to the world! The saviour reigns
   F   G7   C
Let men their songs employ
      F C   F C
While fields and floods, rocks, hills, and plains

Repeat the sounding joy
 G7
Repeat the sounding joy
   C   F   G7   C
Repeat, repeat the sounding joy!

C   G7   C
He rules the world with truth and grace
   F   G7 C
And makes the nations prove
     F C   F C
The glories of His righteousness

And wonders of His love
  G7
And wonders of His love
    C   F   G7 C
And wonders, and wonders of His love

37. Auld Lang Syne

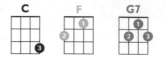

C   **G7**
Should auld acquaintance be forgot
  C   **F**
And never brought to mind
   C   **G7**
Should auld acquaintance be forgot
  F **G7** **C**
For the sake of auld lang syne

  CHORUS:
  C   **G7**
  For auld lang syne, my dear
    C **F**
  For auld lang syne
    C   **G7**
  We'll take a cup of kindness yet
    F **G7** **C**
  For the sake of auld lang syne

  REPEAT CHORUS

(Mike's Favourite Verse)
C   **G7**
There was a man called Mr Lang
  C   **F**
He had a neon sign
  C   **G7**
And Mr Lang was very old
  F **G7** **C**
So they called it Old Lang's Sign!

  CHORUS

38. Away in a Manger

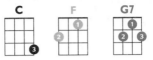

C   **F**
Away in a manger, no crib for a bed
                   C   **F**   **G7**
The little Lord Jesus lay down His sweet head
   C   **F**
The stars in the bright sky looked down where He lay
           C   **G7**   **C**
The little Lord Jesus a-sleep on the hay

                           F
The cattle are lowing the baby a-wakes
                C   **F**   **G7**
The little Lord Jesus, no crying He makes
 C   **F**
I love Thee Lord Jesus, look down from the sky
            C   **G7**   **C**
And stay by my bedside till morning is nigh

                             F
Bless all the dear children in Thy tender care
          C   **G7**   **C**
And fit us for heaven to live with Thee there

39. The Bear Went over the Mountain

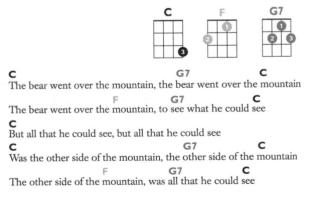

C   **G7**   **C**
The bear went over the mountain, the bear went over the mountain
                     F   **G7**   **C**
The bear went over the mountain, to see what he could see
C
But all that he could see, but all that he could see
C   **G7**   **C**
Was the other side of the mountain, the other side of the mountain
                    F   **G7**   **C**
The other side of the mountain, was all that he could see

40. O Little Town of Bethlehem

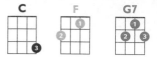

```
G7 C       G7 C              F   G7     C
O little town of Bethlehem how still we see thee lie
G7 C          G7 C                F   G7     C
Above thy deep and dreamless sleep the silent stars go by
         G7        C G7    C        G7
Yet in thy dark streets shineth the everlasting Light
      C            G7 C        F   G7     C
The hopes and fears of all the years are met in thee tonight


G7  C      G7 C          F      G7  C
How silently, how silently the wondrous gift is given
G7 C         G7 C            F      G7  C
So God imparts to human hearts the blessings of His Heaven
         G7     C G7    C           G7
No ear may hear His coming, but in this world of sin
      C            G7 C            F        G7  C
Where meek souls will receive him still, the Lord God enters in


G7 C       G7  C          F   G7     C
O holy Child of Bethlehem descend to us, we pray
G7  C         G7 C         F   G7  C
Cast out our sin and enter in. Be born to us today
         G7      C G7    C                 G7
We hear the Christmas angels the great glad tidings tell
   C          G7 C            F      G7  C
O come to us, abide with us our Lord Emmanuel


G7 C       G7 C          F     G7  C
O come to us, abide with us our Lord Emmanuel
```

Watch the tricky 1 strum changes from G7 to C

41. Streets of Laredo (Cowboy's Lament)

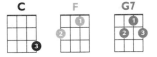

C   F   C   G7
As I walked out on the streets of Laredo
 C   F   C   G7
As I walked out in Laredo one day
 C   F   C   G7
I spied a young cowboy all dressed in white linen
C   F   G7   C
Wrapped in white linen and as cold as the clay

   C   F   C   G7
Oh, beat the drum slowly play the fife lowly
C   F   C   G7
Play the Dead March as you carry me along
   C   F   C   G7
Take me to the green valley and lay the sod o'er me
   C   F   G7   C
For I'm a young cowboy and I know I've done wrong

C   F   C   G7
I see by your outfit that you are a cowboy
   C   F   C   G7
These words he did say as I boldly stepped by
   C   F   C   G7
Come sit down beside me and hear my sad story
   C   F   G7   C
I was shot in the breast and I know I must die

   C   F   C   G7
Let sixteen gamblers come handle my coffin
   C   F   C   G7
Let sixteen cowboys come sing me a song
   C   F   C   G7
Take me to the graveyard and lay the sod o'er me
 C   F   G7   C
For I'm a poor cowboy and I know I've done wrong

42. We Wish You a Merry Christmas

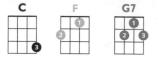

C
                       F
We wish you a Merry Christmas
                  G7
We wish you a Merry Christmas
      C   F
We wish you a Merry Christmas
    G7   C
And a Happy New Year

    CHORUS:
                      G7
    Good tidings we bring
       F   G7
    To you and your kin
        C
    We wish you a Merry Christmas
        G7   C
    And a Happy New Year

C
                   F
We all like figgy pudding
              G7
We all like figgy pudding
      C   F
We all like figgy pudding
  G7   C
So bring some out here

C
                          F
We won't go until we've got some
                      G7
We won't go until we've got some
      C   F
We won't go until we've got some
  G7   C
So bring some out here

    REPEAT VERSE 1 AND CHORUS

43. Silent Night

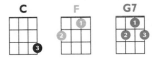

C
Silent night, Holy night
G7   **F**   **C**
All is calm, all is bright
F   **C**
Round yon Virgin Mother and Child
F   **C**
Holy Infant so tender and mild
G7   **C**
Sleep in heavenly peace
          G7   **C**
Sleep in heavenly peace

C
Silent night, Holy night!
G7   **F**   **C**
Shepherds quake at the sight
F   **C**
Glories stream from heaven afar
F   **C**
Heavenly hosts sing Alleluia!
G7   **C**
Christ, the Saviour is born
          G7   **C**
Christ, the Saviour is born

C
Silent night, Holy night
G7   **F**   **C**
Son of God, love's pure light
F   **C**
Radiant beams from Thy holy face
F   **C**
With the dawn of redeeming grace
G7   **C**
Jesus, Lord at Thy birth
          G7   **C**
Jesus, Lord at Thy birth

Count 1, 2, 3 and play down strums on beats 2 & 3 only

44. This Train

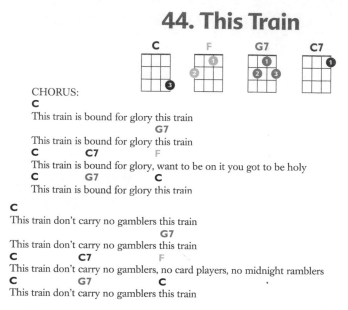

CHORUS:

C
This train is bound for glory this train
                    G7
This train is bound for glory this train
C   **C7**   **F**
This train is bound for glory, want to be on it you got to be holy
C   **G7**   **C**
This train is bound for glory this train

C
This train don't carry no gamblers this train
                         G7
This train don't carry no gamblers this train
C   **C7**   **F**
This train don't carry no gamblers, no card players, no midnight ramblers
C   **G7**   **C**
This train don't carry no gamblers this train

CHORUS

45. Michael Row the Boat Ashore

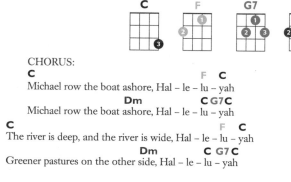

CHORUS:
C   **F** **C**
Michael row the boat ashore, Hal – le – lu – yah
                Dm   **C G7 C**
Michael row the boat ashore, Hal – le – lu – yah
C   **F** **C**
The river is deep, and the river is wide, Hal – le – lu – yah
                Dm   **C G7 C**
Greener pastures on the other side, Hal – le – lu – yah

CHORUS

C   **F** **C**
Jordan's river is chilly and cold, Hal – le – lu – yah
                Dm   **C G7 C**
Chills the body but not the soul, Hal – le – lu – yah

CHORUS

46. Go Tell it on the Mountain

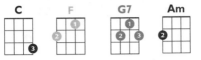

C   F   G7   Am

CHORUS:
C   **Am**
Go tell it on the mountain
F   **G7**   **C**
Over the hills and everywhere
                Am
Go tell it on the mountain
C   **G7**   **C**
Jesus Christ is born

While shepherds kept a-watching
       F   **G7**   **C**
O'er their wandering flock by night

Behold! From out of Heaven
          G7 **C**
There shone a holy light

CHORUS

And lo, when they all saw it
     F   **G7**   **C**
They bowed their heads and prayed

Then travelled on together
         G7   **C**
To where the holy babe was laid

CHORUS × 2

47. Morning Blues

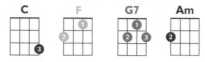

Am   C   Am   C
Woke up early with those morning blues
      Am C   G7   C
Had an aching head that I wished I could lose
  Am   C   Am C
I looked in the mirror, nearly died of fright
    Am   C   G7   C
Those morning blues, ten times worse than last night

CHORUS:
              F   CG7
I got the morning blues – hurt so bad
Am   C   G7   C
Honey come and love me, they're the worst I ever had
Am   C   G7   C
Honey come and love me, they're the worst I ever had

      Am   C   Am   C
Well a nickel's worth of grease and a dime's worth of lard
Am   C   G7   C
I would buy more but the times is too hard
Am   C   Am   C
I don't see why I have to work so hard
    Am   C   G7   C
I can live off the chickens in my neighbour's yard

CHORUS

      Am   C   Am   C
Well I've been in the army and I've been in love
Am   C   G7 C
I used to fly high like a turtle dove
      Am   C   Am   C
And I've had these blues for just the longest time
    Am   C   G7   C
It's just some girl upon this poor boy's mind

CHORUS

48. Will the Circle Be Unbroken?

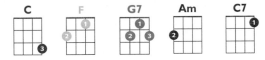

CHORUS:
```
C                    C7
Will the circle be unbroken?
    F                C
By and by, Lord, by and by
                      Am
There's a better home a-waiting
    C       G7   C
In the sky, Lord, in the sky
```

```
C                  C7        F              C
I was standing by the window one dark and cloudy day
                    Am        C      G7    C
When I saw that hearse come rolling for to carry my mother away
                    C7        F              C
Well, I told the undertaker, "Undertaker, please drive slow
                      Am        C      G7    C
For this body that you're hauling, Lord, I hate to see her go"
```

CHORUS

```
C                  C7        F              C
I followed close behind her, tried to hold up and be brave
                    Am        C      G7    C
But I could not hide my sorrow when they laid her in the grave
                    C7        F              C
I went home, our home is lonely now our mother she has gone
                    Am        C      G7    C
All my brothers, sisters crying and of comfort they find none
```

CHORUS

49. Oh Come, All Ye Faithful

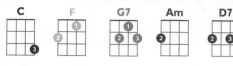

C | F | G7 | Am | D7

C   **G7**   **C**   **G7**
Oh come, all ye faithful, joyful and triumphant
    Am   **G7**   **D7** **G7**
Oh come ye, Oh come ye to Bethlehem
C   **F**   **C**   **F**   **G7**
Come and behold him, born the King of angels

        CHORUS:
          C
        Oh come, let us adore him
          G7
        Oh come, let us adore him
        F   **G7**   **C** **G7**   **C**
        Oh come, let us adore him, Christ the Lord

          G7   **C**   **G7**
Sing, choirs of angels, sing in exultation
Am   **G7**   **D7**   **G7**
Sing, all ye citizens of heaven above
C   **F C** **F**   **G7**
Glory to God in the highest

        CHORUS

C   **G7**   **C**   **G7**
Yea, Lord, we greet thee, born this happy morning
Am   **G7**   **D7** **G7**
Jesus, to thee be glory given
C   **F**   **C** **F**   **G7**
Word of the Father, now in flesh appearing

        CHORUS

50. Ukulele Lady

C   A♭7   G7   Am   Em7   F7   Cmaj7   C6   F   D7

C   **A♭7 G7 C**
I saw the splendour of the moonlight, on Hono…lu…lu Bay
                                       A♭7 G7 C
There's something tender in the moonlight, on Hono…lu…lu Bay
Am   **Em7**
And all the beaches are full of peaches, who bring their "ukes" along
C   **F7**   **G7**
And in the glimmer of the moonlight, they love to sing this song

CHORUS:
C   **Cmaj7**   **C6**   **Cmaj7**   **C**   **Cmaj7**   **C6 Cmaj7**
If you like a Ukulele Lady, Ukulele Lady like-a-you
 F   **G7**   **F**   **G7**   **F**   **G7**   **C**
If you like to linger where it's shady Ukulele Lady linger too
    Cmaj7 C6   **Cmaj7 C**   **Cmaj7**   **C6**   **Cmaj7**
If you kiss a Ukulele Lady, While you promise ever to be true, true, true
 F   **G7**   **F**   **G7**   **F**   **G7 C**
And she see another Ukulele Lady fool around with you
F   **C**   **D7**   **G7**
Maybe she'll sigh – Maybe she'll cry – Maybe she'll find somebody else, Bye and bye…
    C   **Cmaj7 C6**   **Cmaj7 C**   **Cmaj7**   **C6 Cmaj7**
To sing to, when it's cool and shady, where the tricky Wickie Wackies woo
 F   **G7**   **F**   **G7**   **F**   **C**
If you like a Ukulele Lady, Ukulele lady like-a-you.

C   **A♭7**   **G7 C**
She used to sing to me by moonlight, on Hono…lu…lu Bay
C   **A♭7 G7 C**
Fond mem'ries cling to me by moonlight, although I'm far a – way
Am   **Em7**
Some day I'm going where eyes are glowing, and lips are made to kiss
C   **F7**   **G7**
To see somebody in the moonlight and hear the song I miss.

CHORUS

Last line of chorus – last time:
 F   **G7**   **F**   **G7**   **F**   **G7**   **C**   **G7**   **C**   **G7**
If you like a ukulele lady, ukulele lady like a me like you, like me like you,
    C   **G7**   **C G7 C**
like me like you like you

Similarity between Ukulele and Guitar

Remove the two thickest strings from a 6-string guitar and you create a tenor guitar. Now you have only 4 strings to worry about; the chords are the same but they are easier to play.

Shorten your tenor guitar a little and you have a baritone ukulele: same 4 strings, same finger work.

Shorten your baritone ukulele and tune the strings up and you have a tenor, concert or soprano ukulele. The same fingering works but it now sounds higher, as if you clipped a capo over the strings on the 5th fret of your guitar.

Standard ukulele C tuning is 5 notes higher than standard guitar tuning:

- guitar G chord is a ukulele C chord
- guitar C chord is a ukulele F chord
- guitar D7 chord is a ukulele G7 chord

The small soprano ukulele is by far the most common of the family. Its larger cousins, the concert ukulele and the tenor ukulele (the biggest of the three) are most often tuned to the same notes. Their increased size alters the tone and the longer fretboard gives access to more notes, but they cost more and don't fit so easily in a backpack! Before buying, check the sound of bigger ukes and consider what you want to use it for — bigger is not always better.

Guitar G Chord
Ukulele C Chord

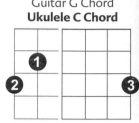

Guitar C Chord
Ukulele F Chord

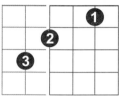

Guitar D7 Chord
Ukulele G7 Chord

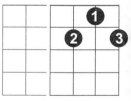

Reading Guitar Chord Boxes for the Ukulele

You've just found your favourite song in a book featuring guitar chords. If you're playing solo you could treat the pictures as ukulele chord boxes by ignoring the two left-hand strings (as shown above). If you're playing a baritone ukulele, you will now be playing the chords as written.

If you are playing a soprano, concert or tenor ukulele with others, you will need to play the chords on the sheet music by their letter name instead of following the pictures. If you haven't learned their shapes, it's a good idea to have a ukulele chord chart with you.

Useful Ukulele Chord Combinations

All the songs in this book are in the key of C or F. If you find these keys difficult to sing, try the chord combinations below for a key that better suits your voice.

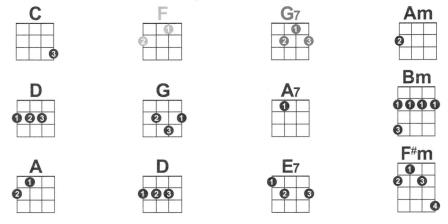

C   F   G7   Am

D   G   A7   Bm

A   D   E7   F#m

The Play-along CD

The play-along CD has samples of all the songs in the book (with some full versions). It provides an easy way to learn the songs while giving you a vocal and ukulele to follow and a band of musicians to back you. The tempo of the songs is lively and they are played at their normal speed so the CD is fun to listen to.

Using the CD

Without the ukulele:

1. Listen to the CD as often as you can to learn the lyrics and tunes.

2. Using the book and CD, sing the chord names to the tune of the song you are learning.

   e.g. Polly Wolly Doodle would go like this:

   F
   Yellow yellow yellow, yellow yellow yellow
                            C
   Yellow yellow yellow, yellow red

   Red red red, red red red
             F
   Red red red, red yellow

With the ukulele:

1. Without strumming, sing the chord names with the CD while fingering the chord shapes and getting used to changing between chords.

2. Strum the song while singing. If you find the tempo too fast, switch the CD off, slow everything down and practise until you are comfortable.

3. Slowly bring the song up to speed as your skill improves.

4. Play along with the CD at full speed and, when you can, sing the song lyrics.

CD Track Listing

1. Tuning Track
2. Row, Row, Row Your Boat
3. Christmas Is Coming
4. Three Blind Mice
5. Frère Jacques/R2D2/Young Bart Simpson
6. Polly Wolly Doodle
7. It Ain't Gonna Rain No More
8. Miss Mary Mac
9. The Ballad of Eensy Weensy
10. Oh, Dear! What Can the Matter Be?
11. Mary Had a Little Lamb
12. Hush Little Baby
13. Rock My Soul
14. The Farmer's in the Dell
15. Blow the Man Down
16. This Old Man
17. London Bridge Is Falling Down
18. Shortnin' Bread
19. Li'l Liza Jane
20. Buffalo Girls
21. He's Got the Whole World in His Hands
22. Michael Finnigan
23. I Saw Three Ships
24. Clementine
25. O Christmas Tree (O Tannenbaum)
26. Skip to My Lou, My Darling
27. Alouette
28. 'Twas the Night Before Christmas
29. Hail! Hail! The Gang's All Here
30. Oh, Susanna
31. Angel Band
32. Banks of the Ohio
33. Home on the Range
34. Five Little Monkeys
35. Frog Went a Courtin'
36. Jingle Bells
37. Joy to the World
38. Auld Lang Syne
39. Away in a Manger
40. The Bear Went over the Mountain
41. O Little Town of Bethlehem
42. Streets of Laredo (Cowboy's Lament)
43. We Wish You a Merry Christmas
44. Silent Night
45. This Train
46. Michael Row the Boat Ashore
47. Go Tell it on the Mountain
48. Morning Blues
49. Will the Circle Be Unbroken?
50. Oh Come, All Ye Faithful
51. Ukulele Lady
52. Strumming Track
53. Chord Patterns

Index of Page Numbers

64